Hello, Family Members,

Learning to read is one of the m of early childhood. **Hello Reac** children become skilled reade readers learn to read by remembering frequently used words like "the," "is," and "and"; by using phonics skills to decode new words; and by interpreting picture and text clues. These books provide both the stories children enjoy and the structure they need to read fluently and independently. Here are suggestions for helping your child.

- Have your child think about a word he or she does not recognize right away. Provide hints such as "Let's see if we know the sounds" and "Have we read other words like this one?"
- Encourage your child to use phonics skills to sound out new words.
- Provide the word for your child when more assistance is needed so that he or she does not struggle and the experience of reading with you is a positive one.
- Encourage your child to have fun by reading with a lot of expression . . . like an actor!

I do hope that you and your child enjoy this book.

— Francie Alexander
Chief Education Officer,
Scholastic's Learning Ventures

Activity Pages
In the back of the book are skill-building activities. These are designed to give children further reading and comprehension practice and to provide added enjoyment. Offer help with directions as needed and encourage your child to have FUN with each activity.

Game Cards
In the middle of the book are eight pairs of game cards. These are designed to help your child become more familiar with words in the book and to play fun games.
- Have your child use the word cards to find matching words in the story. Then have him or her use the picture cards to find matching words in the story.
- Play a matching game. Here's how: Place the cards face up. Have your child match words to pictures. Once the child feels confident matching words to pictures, put cards face down. Have the child lift one card, then lift a second card to see if both match. If the cards match, the child can keep them. If not, place the cards face down once again. Keep going until he or she finds all matches.

For Melissa Torres and Patti Ann Harris
with thanks for their 'beary' good work.
—J.H.

For Daddy and Mom, from whom I inherited
both my love of art and humor
—P.B.

ISBN: 0-439-32473-4

Text copyright © 2001 by Joan Holub.
Illustrations copyright © 2001 by Priscilla Burris.
All rights reserved. Published by Scholastic Inc.
SCHOLASTIC, HELLO READER, CARTWHEEL BOOKS, and associated logos are trademarks and/or registered trademarks of Scholastic Inc.

Library of Congress Cataloging-in-Publication Data available

10 9 8 7 6 5 4 3 2 1   01 02 03 04 05

Printed in the U.S.A.   24
First printing, November 2001

SILLY BEARS

by Joan Holub
Illustrated by Priscilla Burris

· ·

My First Hello Reader!
With Game Cards

· ·

SCHOLASTIC INC.

New York   Toronto   London   Auckland   Sydney
Mexico City   New Delhi   Hong Kong

Brown bears.

Clown bears.

The circus is in town bears.

High bears.

Low bears.

Putting on a show bears.

Space bears.

Race bears.

Running to first base bears.

Plane bears.

Train bears.

Dancing candy cane bears.

Bumble bears.

Stumble bears.

Roly-poly tumble bears.

Small bears.

Tall bears.

Just about to fall bears.

Slide bears.

Glide bears.

Silly side-by-side bears.

Late bears.

Wait, bears!

Don't know how to skate bears.

Rub bears.

Scrub bears.

Bubbles in the tub bears.

Red bears.

Bed bears.

Lots of sleepyhead bears.

Pillow fight bears.

Sleep tight, bears. . . .

Time to say GOOD NIGHT,
bears!

Word Find Fun

Can you circle the words BEAR, SHOW, SILLY, and SLEEP?

Q	G	B	S	D	H
S	I	L	L	Y	K
H	P	B	E	A	R
O	Z	J	E	F	S
W	C	M	P	T	N

Circus Bear

Draw a line to help the bear find his way to the circus.

Rhyme Time

Draw a line from each word
to the picture it rhymes with.

town

plane

plate

rub

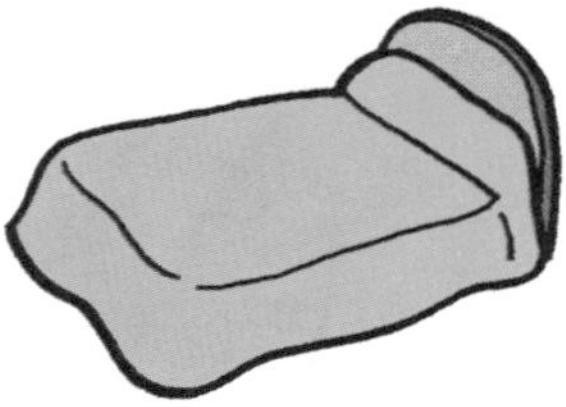

head

Bear Faces

Draw a face on each bear
to show how it is feeling.

Happy

Sad

Silly

Mad

Look-Alikes

Circle the two hats that look exactly the same.

Making Music

Which of these things are used to make music?
Circle each one.

ANSWERS

Word Find Fun

```
Q   G   B  (S)  D   H
(S   I   L   L   Y)  K
 H   P  (B   E   A   R)
 O   Z   J   E   F   S
(W)  C   M  (P)  T   N
```

Circus Bear

This is one possible path.

Rhyme Time

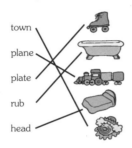

town

plane

plate

rub

head

Bear Faces

Answers will vary.

Look-Alikes

The hats that look exactly alike are:

Making Music

flute

drum

french horn

trumpet